W9-CPY-663

CIRQUE DU FREAK

VOLUME
1

Story: Darren Shan
Manga: Takahiro Arai

CIRQUE DU FREAK 1
CONTENTS

DO YOU THINK THAT'S WEIRD? IT SEEMS LIKE THE ONLY PERSON WHO UNDERSTANDS ME IS MY BEST FRIEND, STEVE.

MY NAME IS DARREN SHAN.

MY FAVORITE THINGS IN THE WORLD ARE...

EVERYONE ELSE JUST GETS CREEPED OUT, BUT I DON'T CARE!

...SPIDERS!

CHAPTER 1: DARREN AND STEVE

THERE'S NO ONE I'D RATHER HANG AROUND WITH!

PERHAPS IT WAS DESTINY THAT DREW US TO THAT CIRCUS.

YES, PERHAPS...

PAPER: CIRQUE DU FREAK

CHAPTER 1:
DARREN AND STEVE

MAN, THEY'RE GOOD!

I *TOLD* YOU IT WAS CRAZY TO CHALLENGE MIDDLE SCHOOLERS ...

DO
(DMM)

TO
(TMP)

S
T
E
V
E
!

YOU
CAN'T
SLIP
THAT
ONE
PAST
ME!

DA
(DASH)

TO

PIIN
(PING)

NEVER FEAR, HOTSHOT SHAN IS HERE!

GYU (ZOOM)

GO, DARREN, GO!

GOAAAAAL!!

WAA (YAHHH)

HEH! THANK YOU, THANK YOU!

GUI (GRAB)

ARE YOU THAT DIRTY THAT YOU CAN'T EVEN KEEP A PROMISE?

CHI (GRIT)

YOU KIDS WILL TAKE FIVE AND APPRECIATE IT.

HEY...

...WASN'T THE BET FOR 10 DOLLARS?

WOO-HOO! 87 STRAIGHT VICTORIES!

LATER.

BOGU (WHOMP)

HEY...

DON'T ASK ME TO...

WE WENT EASY ON YOU SO YOU COULD WIN!

GET OFF ME, KID!

DOSA (FLOP)

FORGET ABOUT THE CIVILIANS, SOLDIER! THE ENEMY IS AT THE TOP OF THIS HILL!

IS YOUR MOM HOME?

OH, DARREN!

DADA (DASH)

I'M ON MY WAY, CAPTAIN!

I THINK I'LL HAVE SOME CAVIAR AND CHAMPAGNE!

WOULD YOU LIKE ANYTHING TO EAT OR DRINK?

DON'T MIND HER.

STEVE...

OKAY, BUT ONLY FOR THREE DAYS.

AT LEAST YOUR MOM IS PRETTY.

I WISH SHE WOULD SWITCH SPOTS WITH YOUR MOM, DARREN.

FRIDAY OF THE DEATH

YEAH, JUST A FEW!

BLOOD VAMPIRE

WOW, DID YOU GET SOME NEW POSTERS?

THE ONE

GO, LITTLE GUY!

ARE YOU KEEP-ING ANY SPIDERS AGAIN?

NOT AFTER THAT TIME I SUCKED THE TARANTULA THEY BOUGHT ME INTO THE VACUUM CLEANER.

NO, MOM AND DAD WON'T LET ME ANY-MORE.

AND YOUR OBSES-SION WITH SPIDERS IS JUST AS BAD!

WONDER WHAT KIND IT IS. AN ORB-WEAVER, MAYBE?

TSUTSUUU (DROOP)

YOU SURE DO LOVE YOUR HORROR STUFF...

A SPI-DER!!

PAA (PZOW)

WOW!

NO, IT CAN BE ANY-THING...

SAY, YOU KNOW HOW YOU HAVE TO USE A STAKE TO KILL A VAMPIRE...?

DOES THE STAKE HAVE TO BE MADE OUT OF WOOD?

14

SFX: GAAAA (RAWRRR)

WAIT,
WHAT'S
...

...

キーン
フーン
キーン
フーン
KIN KON KAN KON
(DING DONG
BING BONG)

AND THEREFORE, ONCE WORLD WAR II HAD EFFECTIVELY CONCLUDED AROUND THE GLOBE...

...THE TOTAL NUMBER OF CASUALTIES WAS MORE THAN 72 MILLION.

YOU'VE REALLY GOT A THIRST FOR VIOLENCE, DON'T YOU, STEVE?

I'LL GET PAID TO FIGHT AND TRAVEL AROUND THE WORLD!

WARS ARE COOL. WHEN I GROW UP, I'M GOING TO BE A MERCENARY!

HEY, DARREN!

WHAT'S THAT?

THAT'S THE BEST PART! IT'S A BATTLE FOR YOUR LIFE!

GO OFF TO WAR, AND YOU'LL WIND UP DEAD.

GOSO (RUSTLE) GOSO

SFX: DADADA (RATTA-RATTA-RATTA)

KUSHA (SKSHH)

HA HA HA.

18

HMM...

HEY!

OH, WELL, I WAS...

ヒョイ
HYOI
(YANK)

OOOH!

PIRA
(FLAP)

ビラ

THAT SOUNDS NEAT! WHERE'D YOU GET THIS?

AND BY "FREAK," I'M GUESSING THEY MEAN FREAKS OF NATURE.

"CIRQUE" IS FRENCH FOR CIRCUS.

CIRQUE DU FREAK, THE CIRCUS OF FREAKS...

WEIRD GUY?

IT'S A CIRCUS!

SOME WEIRD GUY GAVE IT TO ME ON THE WAY HOME FROM STEVE'S HOUSE LAST NIGHT.

THIS LOOKS REALLY COOL!

AND IT'S ONLY RUNNING UNTIL THIS TUESDAY, DARREN!

FLYER: CIRQUE DU FREAK /
LIMITED SHOWING: 8/9 — 8/15 /
$20 PER PERSON

SEE:

SIVE AND
SEERSA—
THE TWISTING
TWINS

THE SNAKE-BOY

THE WOLF-MAN

GERTHA TEETH

LARTEN
CREPSLEY AND
HIS PERFORMING
SPIDER—
MADAM OCTA

ALEXANDER RIBS

THE BEARDED
LADY

HANS HANDS

RHAMUS
TWOBELLIES—
WORLD'S
FATTEST MAN

WARNING!!
SOME RESTRICTIONS
APPLY! NOT FOR THE
FAINTHEARTED!!

WHAT IS THIS?

M-MR. DALTON...

DAR-REN.

DAR-REN.

NBE (BLAH)

ACK!

WHERE DID YOU GET IT!?

I, ER, THAT IS...

WHERE DID YOU GET IT?

IT'S AN ADVERTISEMENT, SIR.

!!

GATA (THUNK)

MR. DALTON, IT'S MINE!

AHA! I SEE, THEN...

I WAS GOING TO ASK YOU ABOUT IT LATER, AT THE END OF CLASS.

I THOUGHT IT LOOKED INTERESTING, SO I PICKED IT UP.

YOURS, STEVE?

SIT DOWN, STEVE, DARREN.

TON (TAP) TON

THAT'S DIFFERENT. NOTHING WRONG WITH AN INQUISITIVE MIND.

THE CON MEN PUT THESE POOR PEOPLE ON DISPLAY AND CALLED THEM FREAKS.

A PERSON WITH THREE ARMS OR TWO NOSES.

SOMEONE WHO DOESN'T LOOK ORDINARY.

AND THESE POOR PEOPLE WERE NO DIFFERENT FROM YOU OR ME, EXCEPT IN LOOKS.

THEY CHARGED THE PUBLIC TO STARE AT THEM AND INVITED THEM TO LAUGH AND TEASE.

HOW AWFUL.

THAT'S CRUEL!

LONG AGO, THERE USED TO BE REAL FREAK SHOWS.

GREEDY CON MEN CRAMMED MALFORMED PEOPLE IN CAGES AND...

SIR, WHAT'S "MALFORMED" MEAN?

QUESTION!

DO YOU THINK THE CIRQUE DU FREAK IS A REAL FREAK SHOW?

FREAK SHOWS WERE BANNED YEARS AGO, BUT EVERY SO OFTEN YOU'LL HEAR A RUMOR...

MR. DALTON!

YOU'D HAVE TO BE REALLY TWISTED TO WANT TO GO TO ONE OF THOSE!

...

STILL, IF IT WAS REAL, I WOULD HOPE NOBODY HERE WOULD DREAM OF GOING.

I DOUBT IT; PROBABLY JUST A CRUEL HOAX.

HEY, DARREN!

HAA (SIGH)

SEE YOU TOMOR-ROW!

I'LL BE KEEPING THIS FLYER.

STEVE IS CORRECT.

JIRIIIIII (RIIIING)

GATA (THUMP)

GATA

KIN KON
(DING
DONG)

WE'RE
GOING!

WELCOME
HOME,
DARREN.

HI,
MOM!

POI-
(TOSS)

AND
REMEM-
BER TO
TAKE
YOUR
BATH!

SORRY,
MOM!

TOTATA
(TROMP)

DON'T
TOSS
YOUR BAG
ON THE
FLOOR!

HEY!
DAR-
REN!

24

THIS IS GONNA BE THE COOLEST THING EVER!

KYU (SKRK)

ZABAA (SPLOSH)

FLYER: RHAMUS TWOBELLIES—WORLD'S FATTEST MAN

I SAID I WANTED IT FOR MY BEDROOM WALL.

HUH?

WHAT DID YOU SAY TO HIM?

BUT HEY, AT LEAST YOU CONVINCED HIM TO GIVE THE FLYER BACK!

TOO BAD MR. DALTON SNIPPED OFF THE ADDRESS.

ADULTS WILL DO ANYTHING AS LONG AS YOU BUTTER THEM UP!

GAA (GRARR)

HE'S WAY TOO SOFT ON YOU!

ARE YOU KIDDING ME?

IT'S $20 FOR A TICKET, RIGHT?

WHAT ABOUT THE MONEY?

YEAH!! THERE'S NO WAY WE'RE MISSING THIS!!!

SO WHAT'S THE PLAN? ARE WE ALL GOING?

OUR HERO!

HA-HA-HA-HA

STEVE THE GREAT!

ALL MEMORIZED!

OOOO COOOO

OH YEAH!

WHAT ABOUT THE DIRECTIONS?

WHY DO YOU THINK WE PLAY SOCCER FOR MONEY?

WE'VE GOT $200 JUST FROM THAT!

SEE YOU TOMORROW! HOPE YOU'RE EXCITED!

BISHI (GRIN)

I'LL SNEAK OUT AT NIGHT AND BUY US THE TICKETS!

CIRQUE DU FREAK...

FLYER: PERFORMING SPIDER — MADAM OCTA

...HAS TO BE THE SPIDER ...

THE ONE I WANT TO SEE THE MOST...

HE WANTS TO GO MOST OF ALL!

"YOU'D HAVE TO BE TWISTED TO WANT TO GO TO A FREAK SHOW," INDEED!

GOSHI (RUB)

GOSHI

MOGU (MUNCH) MOGU

モグ モグ

GA (CHOMP)

GA

WHAT A GOOD BOY! HE EVEN TOOK HIS DISHES TO THE SINK.

JIIII (STARE)

じ〜〜〜

ALL DONE! THAT WAS GOOD.

NOTHING'S WRONG.

WHAT'S WRONG WITH YOU? YOU'RE HIDING SOMETHING!

ピンポォン

PINPONNN (DING-DONGGG)

I DON'T KNOW. LET'S HOPE HE DOESN'T GET ANY STRANGER!

WHY IS DARREN ACTING SO STRANGE?

SMASH

I'M HOME!

HI, DADDY!

TURN IT DOWN, DARREN.

YOU'RE HOME LATE, DERMOT. WE ALREADY ATE DINNER.

OKAY!

GONYO (WHISPER) GONYO

OH, FINE! BUT ONLY IF YOU DON'T TELL MOM AND DAD!

IT HAPPENS! NIGHT, DAD.

TATA (TMP TMP)

WELL, WELL! ON GOOD BEHAVIOR TODAY, DARREN?

BUZZ OFF, ANNIE!

TELL ME, DARREN!

GOOD NIGHT, SLEEP TIGHT...

YOU'RE JUST A KID TOO!

SORRY! NO KIDS ALLOWED.

BATAN (THUMP)

I WANT TO SEE IT TOO!

WELL? HOW DID IT GO!?

TELL US, STEVE!

WELL? WELL? WELL!?

SHOW US THE TICKETS!

SHHHH!!

I HAVE SOME GOOD NEWS AND SOME BAD NEWS.

COME ON, STEVE, DON'T MESS AROUND WITH US. DID YOU GET THEM OR NOT?

ビリ (RIP)

BIRI

ビリ BIRI

TOO MANY PEOPLE HERE.

I'LL TELL YOU AFTER SCHOOL.

WE DON'T WANT ANYONE HEARING, DO WE?

ニ/ョキ JOKI

ニ/ョキ JOKI (KCHK)

ニ/ョキ

THAT'S ALL OF THEM?

OOOH!!

HUH?

AS YOU CAN SEE, I'VE GOT THE TICKETS!

FIRST, THE GOOD NEWS.

TICKETS: CIRQUE DU FREAK

YEP, THAT'S THE BAD NEWS.

HUH...?

THESE WERE THE ONLY TWO I COULD GET.

...WHO GETS THE TICKETS?

S-SO...

SOLD OUT!?

IN FACT, THESE WERE THE LAST TWO TICKETS BEFORE THE SHOW WAS SOLD OUT.

YOU'VE GOTTA BE KIDDING ME!

GAAN (DONGG)

I CAN'T BELIEVE IT!

HE SNUCK OUT OF THE HOUSE AT NIGHT TO BUY THEM, SO HE HAS TO GET ONE. AGREED, ALAN, TOMMY?

WELL, STEVE HAS TO GET ONE.

HMMM...

ONE FOR ME, THEN.

ピッ (TWIK)
PI

AGREED.

UH, A-AGREED.

SO THAT'S WHAT YOU WERE MAKING DURING CLASS...

シャカ

シャカ

YEP! I'M PUTTING THE OTHER TICKET IN HERE AND SHAKING IT UP.

SFX: SHAKA (SHAKE) SHAKA

PAKA (THWUP)

NICE AND FAIR!

AS A MATTER OF FACT, I'VE ALREADY THOUGHT OF A WAY TO DETERMINE WHO GETS THE OTHER TICKET.

プルッ プルッ

GOSO (RUSTLE) GOSO

NO ROUGH STUFF!

ALL RIGHT! NO HARD FEELINGS.

AGREED!

I LIKE IT! SOUNDS FUN!

ARE YOU IN, GUYS?

I'LL OPEN THE CASE AND DROP THEM ALL FROM ABOVE!

WHOEVER GRABS THE TICKET FIRST WINS!

HOW'S THAT?

GOKURI (GULP)

ONE, TWO...

...THREE!!

BUWA (BWOOSH)

I CAN'T FIND IT ANYWHERE!

IT'S NOT HERE!

HUH? DID I JUST...

WHAT'S IN YOUR HANDS, DARREN?

LET'S TAKE A LOOK-SEE.

MAYBE SO, BUT THERE'S SOMETHING IN THOSE FISTS OF HIS.

HE HAD HIS EYES SHUT!

HE DOESN'T HAVE IT. HE CAN'T HAVE.

DOKI (BA-THUMP)

ドキ

ドキ

DOKI

...

WHAT ABOUT THE OTHER HAND?

...

PA (SHWIK)

YESSSSS!

GOAAAAL!!

HA HA HA HA!

TICKET: CIRQUE DU FREAK

YEAH, I CONVINCED THEM I WAS STAYING AT YOUR HOUSE!

WERE YOUR PARENTS OKAY WITH IT?

THANKS FOR WAITING!

LET'S NOT DISCUSS THIS...

MUST BE HARD WITH TWO PARENTS. I'VE ONLY GOT *HER* TO WORRY ABOUT—HALF THE TROUBLE!

IT'S LIKE AN ADVEN-TURE!

MAN, I'M SO EXCITED!

ENJOY IT FOR US!

HAVE A GOOD TIME!

SORRY ALAN, SORRY TOMMY.

I'LL BUY PLENTY OF SOUVENIRS FOR YOU GUYS!

HEH! GETTIN' SCARED?

SUSU (SLOOP)

ACK! THE ONE THEY SAY IS *HAUNTED* !?

!!

HANG ON A SEC!

M-ME, SCARED? YEAH RIGHT!

AN OLD THEATER ON THE EDGE OF TOWN!

YOU KNOW, THE ONE WHERE THE KID FELL OFF THE BALCONY AND DIED.

WHERE'S THE PLACE, STEVE?

OH NO, FOR REAL!?

DAMN. IT'S MR. DALTON AND THE POLICE.

THEY'RE STAKING THE PLACE OUT TO MAKE SURE NO STUDENTS ARE GOING.

CHI (TSK)

HE MUST HAVE USED THE MAP ON THE FLYER.

HOW DARE YOU HAND THESE OUT!

AND TO CHILDREN!

...

GUWAA (GRARRG)

PUKUU (PSHHT)

HOW CAN THIS BE HAPPENING...

AFTER ALL OUR HARD WORK...

HEY, CHECK IT OUT!

38

HE'S GETTING AWAY! AFTER HIM!

TATATA (TMP)

ARE YOU ALL RIGHT, SIR!?

WHAT'S WITH THE TINY GUY?

PUT ME DOWN!

AAH!

POI (TOSS)

WAIT, DARREN!

THIS IS CRAZY!

DA (DASH)

LET'S GO, STEVE!

WE'VE GOT TO FOLLOW HIM!

OH!!

PETATATA (PUT)

HE'S SO DAMN FAST!

BUT HOW!?

HA (HUFF)

HA

UH, UH, UH...

T-THEN HURRY UP!

S-S-SCARED, ME!? NO WAY!

ARE YOU SCARED OR SOMETHING!?

HURRY UP, DARREN! MR. DALTON'S GONNA COME RUNNING THIS WAY!

ZOZO (SHIVER)

W-WHOA...

YOU ARE SO SIMPLE-MINDED.

MERARA (BLOOM)

LET'S GO IN!

OKAAAY!

HIYAAAH!!

GORO (ROLL)

GORO

PARA (CRINK)

WELL, WELL. CAN I HELP YOU BOYS?

!!!

I THINK MY EYES ARE GETTING USED TO THE DARK ...

...NESS!?

IT WAS WARM OUT-SIDE...

WHY IS IT SO COLD?

DON (THUMP)

....

IT'S PITCH-BLACK...

BATAN (THUMP)

GOOOO
(WHOOOOSH)

!?

VERY
WELL.

AAAH.

HMM,
YOU ARE
VERY LATE,
BOYS.

TICKETS,
PLEASE.

MMMMM.

OH!

??

SFX: GOKUKU (GULP)

SFX: PAKU (CHOMP)

SO WE
WILL
MAKE AN
EXCEP-
TION.

NORMALLY,
WE DON'T
WELCOME
CHILDREN,
BUT I CAN
SEE YOU ARE
TWO FINE,
COURAGEOUS
YOUNG MEN.

SHAAAA
(SHHHK)

YOU
MAY
GO IN
NOW.

LOOK, STEVE! OPEN SEATS!

CHILL OUT, DARREN.

ZAWA ZAWA (MURMUR)

GAYA (YAMMER)

WHAT A PERFECT VIEW!

SUUU (SHHH)

THEY'RE STARTING!

SFX: DOKI (BA-BUMP) DOKI

I RECKON HE WAS A REAL MIND-READER.

WOW, THAT WAS JUST LIKE WHAT THAT GUY DID!

SO, STEVE, I WAS THINKING...

I BET YOU ANY-THING YOU LIKE THEY DON'T SELL POPCORN.

...HOME OF THE WORLD'S MOST REMARK-ABLE HUMAN BEINGS!

...WELCOME TO THE CIRQUE DU FREAK...

LADIES AND GENTLE-MEN...

BA (FLIK)

I AM YOUR HOST FOR THIS EVENING AND THE OWNER OF THIS CIRCUS...

...MR. TALL, AT YOUR SERVICE.

PEKO (BOW)

WE ARE COMMITTED TO ASTOUNDING AND TERRIFYING YOU!

SFX: DOYO (HUSH)

THOSE WHO ARE EASILY SCARED SHOULD LEAVE NOW.

OUR LINE-UP HAS CHANGED MANY TIMES...

...BUT NEVER OUR AIM, I ASSURE YOU.

THE CIRQUE DU FREAK HAS BEEN IN BUSINESS FOR OVER 500 YEARS.

THIS IS NOT SO! EVERY ACT YOU SEE TONIGHT IS REAL!

I'M SURE THERE ARE PEOPLE WHO CAME TONIGHT THINKING OUR FREAKS WOULD BE PEOPLE IN MASKS OR HARMLESS MISFITS...

YOU WILL FORGIVE ME FOR INTRODUCING OUR FIRST ACT IN HUSHED TONES.

BUT ENOUGH SHOUTING FROM ME. THE WORLD'S MOST INCREDIBLE SHOW WILL SOON BEGIN.

AHEM...

PRESENTING TO YOU...

...THE WOLF-MAN.

SHHH.

QUIET!

GAYA (BRRM)

GYA (AAGH)

YOU'RE HURTING ME!

ME TOO!

LET ME TOUCH HIM!

REALLY?

WOW.

SUSU (SWISH)

HEH HEH HEH!

D-DON'T DO IT, STEVE!

HE'LL WAKE UP!

IT SMELLS STRANGE TOO, LIKE BURNING RUBBER.

IT WAS SPIKY... LIKE A HEDGE-HOG.

SFX: WAA (RAHH) SFX: KUN (SNIFF)

PIKU (TWITCH)

ZUDAAN (THWOMP)

EEEEK!

GURURURU
(GRRRRR)

GRAWWWR...

AWOOOOOO!!

BIRI
(BZZ)

BIRI

47

EEK!

ZUDODODO
(ZUOOMM)

NOOOO
!!

GAAAA
(RAWWWR)

MUSHI
(GRSSHT)

!! AAH!

ギョロ ギョロ

AAH!

EEK!

SFX: GYORO (SPIN)

ゴゴゴ

SFX: GONYO (WHISPER) GONYO

AAH!

EEEH!

ダラ

ダラン...
(BLONGG)

AAH!

EEK!

タタッ TATA (TSHH)

KIRA (KLING)

SFX: PARA (SPRINKLE) PARA

SHA (SHK)

SHA

SHA

T-THAT'S THE GUY WHO LIFTED MR. DALTON OFF HIS FEET...

SFX: BURU (SHIVER) BURU

OH, GOOD...

OOOH!

I-IT'S MOVING! I CAN MOVE MY FINGERS!

SUU (SHFFF)

TH-THANK YOU...

PUTSUN (SNAP)

BAAN (TA-DAA)

PLEASE FOLLOW OUR RULES, LADIES AND GENTLE-MEN!!

GO. (GRAHH)

IF YOU CANNOT ACCEPT THAT, LEAVE. LEAVE NOW, BEFORE IT IS TOO LATE!

WE CANNOT GUARANTEE ANYBODY'S SAFETY.

THIS IS NOT A NICE, SAFE CIRCUS WHERE NOTHING GOES WRONG!

SFX: 2020... (SHIVER)

WHAT, DARREN?

UH, STEVE...?

HA HA...

N-NO WAY...

THE SHOW'S JUST GETTING STARTED!

THIS IS GREAT! YOU DON'T WANT TO GO, DO YOU?

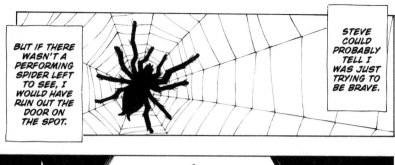

BUT IF THERE WASN'T A PERFORMING SPIDER LEFT TO SEE, I WOULD HAVE RUN OUT THE DOOR ON THE SPOT.

STEVE COULD PROBABLY TELL I WAS JUST TRYING TO BE BRAVE.

The world's fattest man, Rhamus Twobellies!

AFTER THE INCIDENT WITH THE WOLF-MAN...

...THE SHOW PROCEEDED WITHOUT ANY TROUBLE...

Witness the twisting twins, Sive and Seersa!

Alexander Ribs' musical hit medley!

PACHI

Another round of applause for the snake-boy!

YEAH.

HE LOOKS LIKE HE MUST BE OUR AGE!

PACHI (CLAP)

AFTER A TIME, THOUGH, I BEGAN TO FALL UNDER THE CIRCUS'S FREAKY SPELL...

PACHI

Ladies and gentlemen, our next act is another unique and perplexing one.

It can also be quite dangerous, so I ask that you make no noise and do not clap until you are told it is safe.

IT'S FUN, BUT... I DON'T KNOW.

HMM? SURE, I AM.

WHAT'S WRONG? AREN'T YOU HAVING FUN?

IT'S KIND OF BORING.

Mr. Crepsley...

...And his performing spider...

...Madam Octaaa!

ZA
(ZSHH)

ABOUT TIME!

NIYA (SMIRK)

ZOWA (ZSHHH)

STE I

STEVE!

SHH!

?

STEVE!

SFX: GATA (SHIVER) GATA

HEY, STEVE...

HUH? HE LOOKS A LOT LIKE THE GUY WHO GAVE ME THE FLYER.

COME ON OUT.

MADAM OCTA IS TRULY AN INCREDIBLE SPIDER.

SHE IS BOTH POISONOUS AND INTELLIGENT.

WHAT'S WITH HIM?

WOW... IT'S HUGE!!!

ZORO (ZOOSH)

GUSA
(GSHH)

BA
(HOP)

MEEEEE
(BAHHH)

DOZULIN
(DWSHHH)

...BUT SHE IS NOT MY PET.

SHE AND I HAVE WORKED TOGETHER FOR MANY YEARS...

NO, IT'S STILL BREATH-ING.

IS IT DEAD?

ZAWA
(MURMUR)

IF I DID NOT HAVE THIS FLUTE, MY LIFE WOULD BE IN DANGER.

ZAWA

THIS FLUTE HERE...

...IS HOW I CONTROL MADAM OCTA.

BUT THE GOAT WILL DIE IN THE END, AFTER ALL...

...SO WE SHALL FINISH IT QUICKLY.

I HAVE TRAINED MADAM OCTA NOT TO KILL OUTRIGHT WITH HER FIRST BITE.

THE GOAT IS MERELY PARALYZED.

GABU (CHOMP)

ZASASASA (ZSHHH)

DO NOT MOVE! REMEMBER YOUR EARLIER WARNING: A SUDDEN NOISE COULD MEAN DEATH!

ZURU (DRAG) ZURU

ズルズル...

KARAN (CLANK)

カラン

AAH!

SHAAA (HSSSS)

シャアア!!

SFX: GOKU (GULP)

IF YOU DO, SHE MIGHT COME AFTER ME.

SFX: SASASASA (SCUTT)

BUT PLEASE...

...DO NOT MAKE ANY LOUD NOISES.

YOU WILL BE SAFE NOW.

BUN! (ZWISH)

BA (WHOOM)

TSUTSUUU (DRIIIP)

!!!!

NO WAY!!

KAPAA (GAAAH)

HYUUU (ZWOOO)

SFX: SASA (SSHH) SASA

SUTA (THOMP)

PUSHAAA (PSHAAAA)

MMM.

PERO (LICK)

SFX: MOCCHA

MOCCHA (MUNCH)

WA (RAHHH)

DELICIOUS! NOTHING TASTIER.

FRESH SPIDER-WEBS ARE A TREAT WHERE I COME FROM.

WHOAAA!

I'D TRADE EVERY-THING I HAVE FOR HER!

I'D DO ANYTHING TO KEEP MADAM OCTA FOR A PET!

YEAH, I SURE DID...

YUSA (SHAKE)

YUSA

THAT WAS INCREDIBLE! AMAZING! DID YOU SEE THAT, STEVE? DID YOU!?

I'VE FINALLY FOUND ONE, AFTER ALL THESE YEARS... A REAL ONE...

BIKI

BIKI (POP)

IT WAS HIM. I'M SURE OF IT. IT WAS *HIM!*

NII (GRIN)

HUH? I'M JUST FINE, STUPID.

ARE YOU...OKAY? FEELING BAD?

GOSHI (RUB)

STEVE?

...

DID THE SPIDER SCARE YOU?

LOOK AT *YOUR* PALE FACE!

PACHI

PACHI (CLAP)

PACHI

PACHI

PACHI

PACHI

PACHI

PACHI

PACHI

PACHI

...

MADAM'S HOUSE

SPIDER

TEETH

I'M TORN!

HOW MUCH IS THIS?

WOW, NEATO!

OOH!

NOW I WISH I'D BROUGHT MORE MONEY TO SPEND, EH, STEVE?

WELL, BOYS, DID YOU ENJOY THE SHOW?

ZORO (MUTTER)

ZORO

HO-HO! YOU'RE A TOUGH PAIR.

A LITTLE, BUT NO MORE THAN ANYBODY ELSE.

YOU WEREN'T SCARED?

GO BACK BY YOURSELF.

THAT WAS SO MUCH FUN!

DAR- REN.

YEAH?

I MADE SURE TO GET PLENTY OF SOUVENIRS!

THEY'LL ALL BE AMAZED!

DOWA
(THUDD)

WHAT?

STEVE!!

WHY NOT, STEVE!?

I'M NOT COMING! I'M STAYING!

YOU HEARD!

DODODODODO
(DMM)

VODODODO

I HAVE TO TELL YOU...

YOU KNOW, DARREN?

...NO MATTER WHAT HAPPENS...

GO
(GWOOSH)

...YOU'LL STILL BE MY—

I COULDN'T HEAR!

WHAT WAS THAT, STEVE!?

BATA... (THUMP)

GAYA

GAYA (YAMMER)

DON (WHAM)

AAH!

OPEN THE DOOR!

DON (WHAM)

DON

HEY, OPEN UP!

NEVER FEAR, HOTSHOT SHAN IS HERE!

C'MON, DARREN!

ARE YOU SCARED OR SOMETHING?

HAA (CHUFF)

HAA

OOO (WHOOSH)

WE'VE GOT TO LEAVE TOGETHER!

HE'S ALWAYS GETTING IN TROUBLE! I'VE GOT TO KEEP HIM SAFE!

HAA (CHUFF.)

HAA

WHOA!

BAN (WHAM)

WE'RE GOING NOW!

HUH?

I CAME OUT ON ONE OF THE BAL-CONIES.

AND
...

STEVE!

DOKUN
(BA-BUMP)

...MR.
CREPS-
LEY!?

WHAT ARE THEY
SAYING?

WHAT
DO YOU
WANT
WITH
ME...

...YOUNG
MAN?

VUR
HORSTON
...
THE
VAMPIRE
!!!

I KNOW
WHO YOU
REALLY
ARE.

MR.
CREPSLEY...
NO...

...THAT THIS CIRCUS WOULD CHANGE MY LIFE FOREVER, AND FOR THE WORSE.

AT THIS MOMENT, I COULD NEVER HAVE DREAMED ...

THE HAND OF DESTINY HAD JUST BEGUN TO TICK.

I HAD ALWAYS BELIEVED THAT STEVE AND I...

...WERE FRIENDS FOR LIFE.

CHAPTER 2:
A DANGEROUS GAME

HUH?

...I'D RATHER BE A VAMPIRE.

BIKIKI (CRACK)

GARARA (GWOOOSH)

PUCHI

PUCHI

PUCHI (SNAP)

3

AAAH!!

GABA
(LURCH)

DARREN! WHAT TOOK YOU SO LONG TO SHOW UP?

TOMMY, ALAN.

!

HOW'D IT GO, THEN!? WE NEED DETAILS!

I KNOW! AND STEVE ISN'T HERE YET EITHER.

WHAT ABOUT YOU, TOMMY?

I COULDN'T SLEEP A WINK LAST NIGHT!

DAMN! WELL, TALK TO YOU AFTER CLASS, DARREN!

HUH? STEVE'S NOT HERE?

STEVE ISN'T AT SCHOOL...

UH-OH, CLASS IS STARTING!

WE'VE BEEN DYING TO HEAR ALL ABOUT IT.

YEAH... AHH...

SFX: KIN KON (DING DONG)

NO COMPLAINING, NOW!

CLASS IS STARTING!

Awwwl!

MR. DALTON HAS GONE ON LEAVE FOR TODAY, SO I'LL BE YOUR SUBSTITUTE.

I WANT YOU TO MAKE ME A VAMPIRE!

BAKI (CRAK)

I RAN AWAY. I LEFT STEVE BEHIND AND RAN FOR MY LIFE...

SFX: GACHA (CLICK)

I'M THE WORST!

!?

WELL, AREN'T WE LATE!

KIN KON
(DING-DONG)

STEVE
LEONARD.

A BIT.

I KNEW IT!

WHAT'S
WRONG,
STEVE? DID
YOU SLEEP
IN TOO?

I-I
WENT
HOME...

WHY?

WHERE DID
YOU GO
AFTER THE
SHOW?

?

BECAUSE YOU TOLD ME TO...

AND IT WOULD BE WEIRD JUST TO WALK BACK TO YOUR HOUSE ALONE, RIGHT?

...

YEAH, IT WAS GREAT.

IT WAS FANTASTIC! WASN'T IT, STEVE?

SO ANYWAYS, HOW WAS THE CIRCUS?

AND WE TOLD ALAN AND TOMMY ABOUT THE CIRCUS.

WE ACTED OUT EVERY PERFORMANCE IN STUNNING DETAIL!

I COULDN'T IGNORE THE FACT THAT STEVE GAVE ME PIERCING GLANCES FROM TIME TO TIME, HOWEVER...

THESE SPIDERWEB POPS ARE TASTY!

PERO (LICK)

PERO (LICK)

BYOON (BOINING)

A RUBBER RIBS DOLL!

THESE SOUVENIRS ARE BRILLIANT!

MAN, I WISH WE COULD HAVE GONE!

TA-DAAA!

DEROOON (BLOING)

SHOW US!

DID YOU BUY SOMETHING FOR YOURSELF, DARREN?

CHECK THIS OUT...

SFX: GOSO (RUSTLE) GOSO

SFX: MU (HRMPH)

DON'T MAKE ME REPEAT MYSELF!

SPIDERS ARE...

WHAT'S WITH YOU AND SPIDERS, ANYWAY?

A SPIDER! I SHOULD HAVE KNOWN.

MOST OF THEIR PREY IS SMALL INSECTS.

THEY DON'T ACTUALLY NEED IT.

PERA

PERA (BLAH)

YOU KNOW HOW SOME SPIDERS HAVE DEADLY POISON? LIKE TARANTULAS!

...COOL! POWERFUL! SMART!

THEY'LL EVEN ATTACK HUMANS IF THEY SENSE DANGER!

BUT SPIDERS KEEP THAT UNNECESSARILY POWERFUL POISON...

...IN CASE THEY FIGHT ANIMALS LARGER THAN THEM!

?

OF COURSE, VERY FEW HAVE POISON STRONG ENOUGH TO KILL A HUMAN...

THEY'RE FEARLESS CHALLENGERS!

YOU COULD SEARCH THE WORLD OVER AND NEVER FIND A BETTER SPIDER!

I BET MADAM OCTA COULD KILL ANY HUMAN WITH HER POISON!

THAT'S THE THING!

WAIT A SECOND! DIDN'T MADAM OCTA KILL A GOAT THAT WAS LARGER THAN A HUMAN?

POWAAN (GLOWWW)

LIKE WHEN MR. CREPSLEY HAD HER IN HIS MOUTH!

BUT YOU SAID THAT OTHER PEOPLE CONTROLLED MADAM OCTA TOO.

OH, YEAH.

CREPSLEY MUST HAVE BEEN CASTING A SPELL WITH THAT FLUTE!

DIDN'T I TELL YOU? HIS FLUTE!

HOW DO YOU THINK HE CONTROLLED THE SPIDER?

IT WAS TELEPATHY.

THAT'S HOW THEY CONTROLLED THE SPIDER, WITH THEIR MINDS.

THE FLUTES ARE JUST FOR SHOW...

TELEPATHY IS WHEN YOU CAN READ SOMEBODY ELSE'S MIND, OR SEND THEM THOUGHTS WITHOUT SPEAKING.

EVERYONE HAS THAT ABILITY TO SOME DEGREE, WHETHER LARGE OR SMALL.

IT'S LIKE WHEN YOU BOTH SAY THE SAME THING AT THE SAME TIME, OR YOU MAKE EYE CONTACT WHEN PLAYING SOCCER.

TELE-PATHY?

YEAH, THAT'S WHAT I THINK.

...OR, MORE LIKELY, YOU NEED THEM TO ATTRACT HER ATTENTION.

SO YOU WOULDN'T NEED MAGIC FLUTES OR SPECIAL TRAINING OR ANYTHING?

YOU MEAN ANYONE CAN CONTROL HER?

...CAN CONTROL HER?

ANYONE...

BUT WHAT IF?

WHAT IF I COULD CONTROL HER?

PITA (STOP)

ANYONE CAN CONTROL MADAM OCTA, WITHOUT SPECIAL POWERS OR TOOLS?

EVEN ME? NO WAY...

LATER!

SEE YA!

AND HERE I AM...

GOKU (GULP)

IT'S STILL EARLY...

THE FREAKS MIGHT STILL BE SLEEPING...

SFX: GI (CREAK)

I'LL FORGET SHE EVER EXISTED!

...I'LL GIVE UP ON MADAM OCTA.

IF THIS DOOR IS LOCKED...

UH.

KIIIII (CREEEEAK)

IT'S OPEN!!

OOOO (WHOOOSH)

SFX: DO DO (BA-DUMP)

SFX: BATAN (THUMP)

NO! FORGET HER!

I HAVE TO GIVE UP ON THE SPIDER AND JUST GO HOME!

ARE YOU AFRAID, DARREN?

DIDN'T YOU WANT TO SEE MADAM OCTA?

MAYBE I SHOULD LEAVE.

KURU (SPIN)

GACHI ガチ

GACHI (SHIVER) ガチ

WHAT THE HELL AM I DOING!?

OH, COME ON!

TA (TMP)

YES-TERDAY WAS THE FINAL PERFOR-MANCE.

THE FREAKS MIGHT HAVE ALREADY LEFT FOR THE NEXT TOWN.

IF THEY'RE NOT HERE, IT'S TIME TO GIVE UP AND GO HOME, DARREN!

I DON'T SENSE ANYONE AROUND.

MAYBE THEY ARE GONE...

OOOO (WHOOOSH)

SPIDERS ACT ALONE...

I'M NOT SCARED. I'M NOT ...

HELLOO?

KUN (SNIFF)

SPI-DERS...

SPIDERS DO NOT FEAR THE DARK.

JI... (FZZ)

IT SMELLS LIKE...

GYUMU (SQUISH)

GURURURU (GRRRL)

GUGU
(GRRG)

SFX: SUU (ZZZ) SUU

HENA
(SLUMP)

HENA

TIME TO
GO...

I CAN'T
TAKE THIS!
I'M DONE!

!!

DO
DO

DO
(BA-DUMP)

DO
DO

BA-
(WHOOSH)

DO
(BA-DUMP)

DO

DO

ARE YOU SCARED OR SOMETHING?

C'MON, DARREN!

ARE YOU SATISFIED YET?

LET'S JUST GO...

SFX: MOZO (RUSTLE) MOZO

ミスター・クレプスリーへ
マダム・オクタは
もらっていく。
お前の正体を知っているぞ。
町中にばらされたく
なければマダムは
あきらめるんだ。
ぼくはスティーブじゃない
スティーブは全然、関係ない！

クモは大切にする

LETTER: MR. CREPSLEY, I KNOW WHO YOU ARE AND WHAT YOU ARE. I HAVE TAKEN MADAM OCTA AND AM KEEPING HER. DO NOT COME LOOKING FOR HER. DO NOT COME BACK TO THIS TOWN. IF YOU DO, I WILL TELL EVERYONE THAT YOU ARE A VAMPIRE AND YOU WILL BE HUNTED DOWN AND KILLED. I AM NOT STEVE. STEVE KNOWS NOTHING ABOUT THIS. I WILL TAKE GOOD CARE OF THE SPIDER.

GAYA
(YAMMER)

GAYA

SORRY! I'M BUSY THIS AFTERNOON!

YOU'RE AS TIRED OF US PLAYING MIDDLE SCHOOLERS, RIGHT?

HEY, DARREN!

WE WERE TALKING ABOUT WHO TO PLAY IN SOCCER TODAY!

HE DOESN'T HANG OUT AS MUCH THESE DAYS.

DON'T YOU THINK, STEVE?

OH, COME ON, DARREN! WE NEED YOU TO...

BIKU (TWITCH)

NOT THIS TIME. I REALLY CAN'T...

PA (MMF)

UH, SORRY ...

YEAH.

YOUR COOKING IS THE BEST, TRUSKA!

I'M HOME!

BATAN (SLAM)

GABU MUSHA
(GRRK MUNCH)

IT'S FEEDING TIME SOON.

HANG ON, GIRL.

MOZO

MOZO
(RUSTLE)

JUST LIKE STEVE SAID, IT TURNED OUT THAT ANYONE COULD CONTROL MADAM OCTA!

AT FIRST, I HAD SEVERAL CLOSE SHAVES, BUT ONCE I GOT THE HANG OF IT, SHE WAS MINE!

THE THEATER WAS DESERTED ONCE MORE.

THE CIRQUE DU FREAK HAD MOVED ON TO ITS NEXT DESTINATION.

AFTER A WHILE, I STOPPED WORRYING.

STILL, I KEPT A CROSS CLOSE AT HAND!

GACHI (SHIVER)

GACHI

I WAS TERRIFIED OF CREPSLEY COMING AFTER ME AT ANY MOMENT.

MADAM OCTA BELONGED TO ME!

YEEE...

YES!

YES! I DID IT! THE LETTER HAD WORKED!

FOR A SPECIAL TREAT, A PIECE OF PIZZA!

MY JOURNAL'S NEARLY FULL OF ENTRIES!

I BOUGHT A PIZZA TO CELEBRATE, AND SHE SCARFED IT DOWN!

BAKU

BAKU (CHOMP)

IT'S THE GREATEST THING EVER. I FEEL LIKE A KING!

SEE YOU TOMORROW!

I CAN PRACTICALLY CONTROL MADAM OCTA PERFECTLY NOW!

DARREN'S ALWAYS LIKE THIS NOW...

MAN, THIS IS BORING...

WANNA PLAY VIDEO GAMES AT MY PLACE?

SURE!

TA (TMP)

DARREN!

HAA HAA

STEVE...

HAA (HUFF)

HAA

YOU WON'T TALK TO ME, AND YOU WON'T MEET MY GAZE! WHAT'S GOING ON?

DON'T PLAY DUMB! YOU'VE BEEN STEERING CLEAR OF ME THESE PAST TWO WEEKS.

WHY HAVE YOU BEEN AVOIDING ME?

WHAT DO YOU MEAN?

106

NO... YOU DIDN'T SEE ANY-THING?

NO, I DIDN'T!

YOU SAW WHAT HAPPENED THAT NIGHT BETWEEN ME AND VUR HORSTON, DIDN'T YOU?

YOU DIDN'T SEE ME TALKING TO VUR HORSTON?

HUH?

HA HA...

DID I EVER TELL YOU YOU'RE A BAD LIAR, DARREN?

I WASN'T THERE, DIDN'T SEE IT, DON'T KNOW WHAT YOU'RE TALKING ABOUT.

LOOK, STEVE, WHATEVER HAPPENED BETWEEN YOU AND MR. CREPSLEY IS YOUR BUSINESS.

UNLESS YOU WERE THERE, HOW WOULD YOU KNOW...

I SAID I WAS TALKING TO *VUR HOR-STON.*

...THAT VUR HORSTON AND LARTEN CREPSLEY ARE ONE AND THE SAME?

OOPS...

YES, IT IS!

WHAT ELSE COULD IT BE!?

NO, THAT'S NOT IT!

YOU HEARD HIM SAY I WAS EVIL!

THAT'S WHY YOU'VE BEEN AVOIDING ME.

I WAS SCARED...

I WANTED TO JUMP DOWN AND SAVE YOU, BUT I WAS TOO AFRAID...

I COULD SEE YOU TREMBLING WHEN MR. CREPSLEY SUCKED YOUR BLOOD, STEVE...

THAT'S CRAZY! NORMAL PEOPLE DON'T THINK THAT WAY!

YOU WANT TO BE A VAMPIRE!?

...I JUST DON'T KNOW WHAT YOU'RE THINKING ANYMORE!

A-AND PLUS...

PA
(FLIK)

THAT SORRY
...
WAS
OVER
THE
TOP.

GEHO
(COUGH)
GEHO

ARE
EVEN YOU
SAYING
I'M EVIL,
NOW!?

SFX: GA (GRRK)

YOU'RE
HURT-
ING ME...
STEVE...

SFX: GUGU (GRRG)

YOU'RE
MY BEST
FRIEND,
DARREN
...

IF YOU
BREAK
UP OUR
FRIENDSHIP...
I DON'T
KNOW WHAT
I'LL DO...

I-I JUST
DON'T
KNOW WHAT
TO DO ANY-
MORE...

WAH!

WAH!

W-WHEN
I THOUGHT
ABOUT YOU...
BECOMING A
V-VAMPIRE
...

I WAS
SCARED
TOO!

HI
HIKKU
(HIC HIC)

BOO HOO
HOO!

WAAHHH!

LIKE WHAT?

COME TO MY HOUSE.

I WANT TO SHOW YOU SOMETHING!

HEY, STEVE!

HIKKU (CHIC)

ヒック

ヒック

HIKKU

THIS IS A SECRET BETWEEN YOU AND ME ONLY!

SHHHH! KEEP IT DOWN!

IS THIS REAL? WHAT'S GOING ON!?

ARE YOU KIDDING ME!?

モゾ モゾ

MOZO (RUSTLE)

MOZO

HEE HEE HEE!

SHE LOOKS JUST THE SAME AS THE ONE IN THE CIRCUS. WHERE'D YOU GET HER?

A PET SHOP? FROM A ZOO?

HA HA HA...

I TOLD YOU TO PIPE DOWN, STEVE!

NO WAY! THE *REAL* MADAM OCTA!?

AHH, I SEE NOW...

KUI (POKE) KUI

I'M STARTING TO THINK I WAS CRAZY TOO...

...BUT THIS CONFIRMS IT! STEALING A VAMPIRE'S PET!

Y'KNOW, I ALWAYS THOUGHT YOU WERE CRAZY, DARREN...

I'M TOO AFRAID, PLUS YOU NEED MORE THAN ONE PERSON.

UMM, NOT QUITE THAT WELL, YET...

CAN YOU MAKE HER SPIN A WEB IN YOUR MOUTH?

HOW WELL CAN YOU CONTROL HER?

SFX: SU (SHH)

READY? HERE GOES!

IF YOU DISTURB MY ATTENTION AND I LOSE CONTROL OF HER, WHO KNOWS WHAT COULD HAPPEN?

BEING QUIET IS VITAL. DON'T SAY ANYTHING.

COME OUT, MADAM OCTA!

SFX: ZORO (CREEP)

HEH HEH!

SCARED?

CLIMB ONTO STEVE!

SFX: KOKU (NOD)

HYUN
(ZWIP)

PUSHU
(PSHT)

SFX: FURI (WIGGLE) FURI

I'M SO GLAD WE MANAGED TO MAKE UP...

HA-HA! STEVE IS SO EXCITED.

GACHA...
(CLICK)

HEY, DARREN!

!?

WHERE'S
MY...

EEK
...

EEYAAAGH!!

DO
(WHAM)

BIKU
(TWIKK)

STOP!

SFX: KASA (SCUTTLE)

SHAA
(HSSS)

116

BACK INSIDE THE CAGE!!!

HAA
(HUFF)

HAA

KASA
(SKITTER)

KASA

ARE YOU OKAY? STEVE?

STEVE?

AAAAHH...

GUTA
(FLOP)

BUT IF HE DOESN'T GET HELP ...

MADAM OCTA'S BEEN TRAINED NOT TO KILL ON THE FIRST BITE.

IS... IS HE... DEAD?

OF COURSE NOT! YOU CAN SEE HIM BREATHING, CAN'T YOU?

I'M SORRY! I WASN'T THINKING ...

WHY DID YOU WALK IN WITHOUT KNOCKING, ANYWAY? YOU ALWAYS KNOCK FIRST!

YOU STUPID MONSTER!

GA (GRRK)

BUN (WHOOSH)

GASHI
(SNAKK)

!?

BUWA
(SWUSH)

SUTO...
(TONK)

TOON (ZOOSHH)

SFX: MOZO (RUSTLE)

NIYARI (NYEH HEH)

HUH ...?

TELL MOM TO CALL AN AMBU- LANCE, ANNIE.

HENA... (FLOP)

GYU (SQUEEZE)

SFX: PIIPOO (WEE-OOH) PIIPOO

SU (SHH)

HURRY!

I-I'M GOING!

ANY ALLER-GIES?

I JUST DON'T KNOW...

NOW, IS YOUR SON DIABETIC OR EPILEPTIC?

I DON'T KNOW; HE'S NOT ACTUALLY MY SON.

NO IDEA. DID YOU SEE THEM, DARREN? TELL THE DOCTOR.

THERE ARE BITE MARKS ON HIS NECK. ANY IDEA WHAT THOSE MIGHT BE FROM?

WELL, THAT'S UNFORTUNATE. IF WE DON'T KNOW THE CAUSE, THERE'S NOT MUCH WE CAN DO TO TREAT THE BOY.

I'M SORRY, OUR KIDS STILL SEEM A LITTLE RATTLED FROM THE EXPERIENCE.

ANNIE?

...

STEVE!

!

MY POOR LITTLE BABY!

WHAT HAVE YOU DONE TO HIM?

SFX: GA (SHOVE)

HAVE YOU HURT MY BOY? HAVE YOU KILLED MY STEVE?

WHAT HAVE YOU DONE!?

DADA (DASH)

AHAHAAA!

AAAAAHH!

SOB, SOB...

PLEASE, YOU MUST SETTLE DOWN!

I'VE BEEN SUCH A BAD MOTHER ...

MY OWN SON HATES ME...

IT IS MY FAULT ...

OKAY?

NO, DAD. YOU DON'T UNDERSTAND...

SHE'S JUST WORRIED ABOUT STEVE.

DON'T PAY ATTENTION TO WHAT SHE WAS SAYING, DARREN. SHE DOESN'T BLAME YOU.

IT'LL BE ALL RIGHT.

IF I HADN'T STOLEN MADAM OCTA AND TRIED TO TRAIN HER...

MERA
(FWOOSH)

SUKU
(STOP)

WHERE
ARE YOU
GOING,
DARREN?

DA (DASH)

I'VE
GOT TO
SAVE
HIM!

NO MORE
RUNNING
AWAY! I'M
NOT LEAVING
STEVE
BEHIND!

AAAH!

GO (WHOOM)

KURU
(SPIN)

DA (DSHH)

HAA
(CHUFF)

HAA

BASA
(FLAP)

BASA

WELL, IT TOOK YOU LONG ENOUGH.

I HAVE BEEN USING THIS PLACE AS MY BED.

I AM AFRAID I DO NOT HAVE MUCH IN THE WAY OF REFRESH-MENTS...

HAH. WHY SO ANGRY?

FUWA (FWUSH)

CREPSLEY!!

HAVE YOU COME TO TAKE MADAM OCTA "BACK"?

MADAM OCTA SAYS SHE LIKED YOU QUITE A BIT...

THAT IS A RUDE THING TO SAY ABOUT A LADY.

I NEVER WANT TO SEE THAT MONSTER AGAIN!

SFX: GATA (SHIVER) GATA

PLEASE!

I WANT YOU TO MAKE HIM BETTER!

A NASTY BUSINESS.

THE ONE KNOWN AS "STEVE LEOPARD"...

SHE BIT STEVE LEONARD!

DO YOU HAVE ANOTHER SLICE OF PIZZA FOR HER?

GOKURI (GULP)

HEH HEH HEH.

127

FOR EVERY POISON THERE EXISTS AN ANTIDOTE.

MAYBE I HAVE A BOTTLE OF SERUM THAT WILL RESTORE YOUR FRIEND'S NATURAL PHYSICAL FUNCTIONS.

I AM JUST A FREAK. REMEMBER?

ME? BUT I AM NOT A DOCTOR.

NO. I KNOW YOU CAN SAVE HIM!

I KNOW YOU HAVE THE POWER!

YOU ARE A CUNNING YOUNG MAN.

I SEE...

CHAPON (SPLISH)

I WAS IMPRESSED WHEN I FOUND MY SPIDER GONE AND YOUR NOTE IN HER PLACE.

I'LL DO ANYTHING! I JUST NEED THAT ANTIDOTE FOR STEVE!

GIVE IT TO ME! I CAN PAY FOR IT!

THAT'S IT! I KNEW IT!

THEN YOU WERE THE ONE WHO GAVE ME THE FLYER FOR THE CIRCUS...

I KNEW THAT I MADE THE RIGHT CHOICE IN SELECTING YOU.

YOU ARE A BOY WHO IS GOING PLACES.

I KNEW EXACTLY WHAT WAS GOING ON AT ALL TIMES.

WHEN DID YOU NOTICE THAT MADAM OCTA WAS GONE?

JIRI (SCRAPE)

GU (RRG)

I WAS SIMPLY OBSERV-ING YOU.

HE-HEH!

OH, BUT NOT FOR FREE. DO YOU REMEMBER WHAT YOU JUST SAID?

"I'LL DO ANY-THING."

...I WILL OFFER YOU THIS ANTIDOTE.

IF YOU SIMPLY MUST HAVE IT...

YOU MUST BECOME A VAMPIRE, DARREN SHAN.

THE ISSUE IS NOT OPEN TO DEBATE.

NO, PLEASE, NOT THAT!

THERE MUST BE ANOTHER WAY...

...WE HAVE NOTHING FURTHER TO DIS-CUSS.

IF YOU WANT TO SAVE YOUR FRIEND, YOU MUST JOIN ME. IF YOU REFUSE...

YOU ARE THE ONLY ONE I WANT, DARREN.

I DO NOT NEED TWO ASSIS-TANTS.

WHY DON'T YOU TAKE STEVE FOR AN ASSISTANT, THEN?

THOSE ARE THE CONSE-QUENCES OF A CHOICE, YOUNG DARREN.

PIKU (TWITCH)

IF I BECOME A VAMPIRE...

...I'LL HAVE TO LEAVE MY FRIENDS AND FAMILY, AND LIVE A LIFE OF DARKNESS...

HEH HEH HEH.

!!

MAKE
ME A
VAMPIRE!

NIYAA
(SMIRK)

JUST THE KIND OF NOBLE STATEMENT BEFITTING OF A VAMPIRE!

BA (WHOOSH)

WELL SPOKEN, DARREN SHAN!

A PRINCIPLED CHOICE WITH NOT A THOUGHT TO YOUR OWN SAFETY OR CONCERN!

YES, HALF. THAT MEANS YOU WILL BE ABLE TO MOVE ABOUT DURING THE DAY. YOU WILL NOT NEED MUCH BLOOD TO KEEP YOU SATISFIED.

THERE IS NO REASON TO RUSH AT THE START. TIME WILL BE PLENTIFUL ONCE YOU HAVE BEEN INDUCTED.

HALF?

LIFT YOUR HANDS.

SU (SHH)

IN RETURN, I WILL MAKE YOU A HALF-VAMPIRE.

YOU WILL BE MY TRAVELING COMPANION.

AND WITH TIME, YOU WILL BECOME A FULL VAMPIRE.

THAT WILL GIVE ME PLENTY OF TIME TO TEACH YOU OUR WAYS.

ZUGU (ZRRK)

THAT MEANS YOU WILL AGE ONLY ONE YEAR FOR EVERY FIVE THAT PASS.

HALF-VAMPIRES AGE AT A FIFTH THE REGULAR RATE.

IT IS GOOD BLOOD.

WE CAN PROCEED.

HAA (HUFF) HAA

リア リア

ゴゴゴ

GOKUN (GULP)

DO NOT BE SUCH A BABY.

A A G H!

YOU WILL FIND THAT MUCH OF IT LIES AHEAD.

GUI (TUG)

GET USED TO THE PAIN.

I JUST WANT YOU TO KNOW THIS.

ZEE (PANT)

HAA

HAA

I...

I AM SURE YOU MEAN THAT.

FAIR ENOUGH.

SFX: ZUBUBU (SPLASH)

SFX: ZUGU (DRIP)

THAT IS EXACTLY WHY I WANT YOU.

YOU'LL NEVER BE ABLE TO TRUST ME! EVER!

IF THE OPPORTUNITY ARISES TO PAY YOU BACK, I'LL TAKE IT!

YOU WILL GROW STRONG, DARREN.

STRONGER THAN ANY HUMAN...

...AND EVEN ANY VAMPIRE.

STRONGER...

STRONGER...

!!!

STEVE LEONARD?

ガチャ
GACHA
(CLICK)

EEEK!!

MY EYES MUST BE PLAYING TRICKS ON ME.

NNG RRGH...

モゾ"
MOZO (RUSTLE)

DOCTOR, COME LOOK AT THIS PATIENT!

MR. LEONARD!?

6

FUN (SNORT)

PIKU (TKK)

THANK YOU...

YOU SAVED STEVE'S LIFE.

THE MARKS...

...THEY'VE ALREADY SEALED UP.

NIYARI (SMIRK)

IT IS A LENGTHY PROCESS. WE MUST TAKE IT SLOWLY.

I DON'T FEEL VERY DIFFERENT...

ALSO, BEING A HALF-VAMPIRE, YOU WILL RECOVER FROM WOUNDS QUICKER THAN HUMANS.

VAMPIRE SPIT HAS HEALING PROPERTIES.

PAN (PAT) PAN

PERO (CLICK)

MY SALIVA HEALED YOUR WOUNDS.

MAKE IT QUICK!

...

HUH ...?

WE ARE DONE HERE. KEEP YOUR ARMS WRAPPED AROUND MY NECK.

WE ARE GOING TO FLIT.

Y-YOU DON'T HAVE TO SHOUT ...

WE WILL BE RACING ALONG AS THOUGH WE ARE FLYING.

FLIT?

TAKE CARE NOT TO FALL OFF.

DOON (BOOOM)

SU (SHH)

RUN, DARREN SHAN!

IT WILL DO YOU NO GOOD!

DAN (THWUD)

I SEE... VERY WELL!

HA HA HA HA HA!

HA HA HA!

YOU ARE A CREA-TURE OF THE NIGHT NOW.

YOU ARE ONE OF US!

YOU WILL SEEK ME OUT AGAIN!

YOU WILL COME CRAWLING ON YOUR KNEES BACK TO ME!

DARREN!

PINPON (DING DONG)

HELLO?

GACHA (CLICK)

WHAT HAVE YOU BEEN DOING BY YOURSELF SO LATE!?

WE'VE BEEN WORRIED SICK!

THE HOSPITAL JUST CALLED! THEY SAID STEVE'S REGAINED CONSCIOUSNESS!

AAH!

GABA (GLOMP)

DARREN!

WELL, I'M GLAD HE'S BETTER.

AND YOU'RE OUT WANDERING LOOSE WHILE BIG THINGS ARE HAPPENING!

W-WHAT'S THE MATTER, ANNIE?

OH, I'M SO GLAD!

HA-HA, YEAH.

SO IT'S A GOOD THING YOU DIDN'T TURN INTO A MUR-DER, BUD!

ANNIE WAS TERRIFIED THAT THEY'D ARREST YOU IF STEVE NEVER WOKE UP.

WHAAAT!?

I WAS SO SURE... YOU WERE GOING TO JAIL...

...BACK TO ME.

YOU WILL COME CRAWL-ING...

I MADE THE RIGHT CHOICE...

I'M BETTER OFF HERE...

I'VE NEVER SEEN YOU SO HUNGRY FOR BREAKFAST!

YEFF, MUM!!

STEVE'S COMING BACK TO SCHOOL TODAY, RIGHT?

HURRY UP, OR YOU'LL BE LATE!

ONE WEEK LATER

GA

=GA (MUNCH)

SFX: MUSHA (CHOMP) MUSHA

!!?

GAKI (GRRK)

KARAN (CLANG)

WAIT, DARREN! DID YOU BRUSH YOUR TEETH?

SEEYA LATER, MOM!

POI (TOSS)

IT'S NOT LIKE I'VE GOTTEN TALLER OR PACKED ON MUSCLE.

MY BODY'S ACTING STRANGE THESE DAYS.

ESPECIALLY BECAUSE STEVE IS RETURNING TO SCHOOL TODAY.

I HAVE TO MAKE SURE PEOPLE DON'T FIND OUT.

THERE'S JUST A FEELING OF RIPPLING STRENGTH THERE NOW.

I CAN TELL MY BODY IS GETTING STRONGER, AND FAST.

IF ANYONE'S SHARP ENOUGH TO NOTICE, IT'LL BE HIM...

I'M TRYING MY BEST TO CONTROL THIS NEWFOUND STRENGTH, BUT IT'S HARD.

GOTTA BE MORE CAREFUL...

WAN

GNOO

WAN (WOOF)

YIKES!

PEKO (BOW)

GYU (ZOOM)

OH MY!

...

PAKU

PAKU (MUHH)

GAYA

GAYA (YAMMER)

WHAT WAS THE HOSPITAL LIKE?

I CAN'T BELIEVE YOU SURVIVED!

DID THEY OPERATE ON YOU?

GOT ANY SCARS?

THEY SOUND LIKE A BUNCH OF QUACKS TO ME.

THEY DON'T KNOW WHY, BUT I MANAGED A QUICK, FULL RECOVERY!

IT'S FUNNY—THE DOCTORS ARE SCRATCHING THEIR HEADS TOO.

HA HA.

NI (GRIN)

I'M AS HARD TO KILL AS A VAMPIRE!

YOU BET!

CON-GRATS ON MAKING IT BACK, STEVE!

DON'T DO IT, STEVE! YOU'RE STILL RECOVERING!

YEAH!

I'M UP FOR SOME SOCCER TOO!

LET'S HIT THE FIELD!

ENOUGH HELLOS FOR NOW, STEVE!

I WANT TO SEE THIS FOR MYSELF!

LET'S GO, THEN!

N-NO, STOP!

IMAG-INE THAT.

N-NO, I JUST GOT LUCKY...

THAT'S INCRED-IBLE...

EVEN THE HIGH SCHOOL KIDS ARE AFRAID OF HIM!

NO-BODY CAN STOP HIM!

YOU SHOULD SEE DARREN THESE DAYS!

ZA

ZAZA (ZSHH)

DAR-REN'S OFF HIS GAME TODAY ...

HAA (HUFF)

HAA

COME ON, DARREN! THE OLD FOGEYS AT THE HOSPITAL COULD OUT-PLAY YOU!

A A A H!

ZUSHA (ZÜSHH)

SFX: CHIRA (PEEK)

D-
... DARREN?

DO (DRIP)

DO

SFX: DOKU (BLUB) DOKU

ZA (ZSHH)

H-HEY...

DARREN?

GOKU

GOKU (GULP)

GOKU

...

JUST
KIDDING
...

E-

I AM THE
VAMPIRE
LORD!

I WILL
SUCK THE
BLOOD
FROM ALL
OF YOU!

I...

POTA
(DRIP)

WHAT ARE YOU THINKING, DARREN?

YOU'RE A NUT, SHAN!

EWWW, THAT'S GROSS!

AHA HA HA!

...I HOPE?

I THINK I FOOLED THEM...

THAT'S NASTY!

S- SORRY, DID I SCARE YOU?

WHAT'S THE BIG IDEA, DAR- REN?

BIRI (CACK)

GI (GRRK)

MY POWER CAME BUBBLING OUT OF ME, AND I WAS SEIZED BY AN UNCONTROLLABLE URGE...

I COULDN'T STOP MYSELF.

JAAA (FSHHH)

...I MIGHT NOT BE ABLE TO REGAIN CONTROL.

THE NEXT TIME SOMETHING LIKE THAT HAPPENS...

YOU WILL COME CRAWLING ON YOUR KNEES BACK TO ME!

I JUST WANT TO RIP THOSE VESSELS OPEN...

FREE THE CRIMSON LIQUID AND DRINK IT DOWN...

NOW, NOW, NOW!!!

I'LL KNOW WHEN TO STOP...

DON'T WORRY, MY DEAR. I WON'T DRINK MUCH...

GYORO
(GYURR)

...BUT I GOT THIS FUNNY FEELING THAT HE WAS THERE TO TAKE YOU AWAY...

I KNOW IT'S STUPID OF ME TO THINK...

GII...
(GREE)

DARREN?

I CAN'T STAY HERE ANY LONGER...

...A MONSTER...

THERE IS A MONSTER INSIDE OF ME...

A MONSTER THAT WILL NOT OBEY MY COMMANDS.

I CAN'T LIVE A NORMAL HUMAN LIFE BATTLING THIS THING.

I HAVE TO LEAVE BEFORE I DO SOMETHING TRULY TERRIBLE...

BEFORE I KILL MOM, OR DAD...OR MY FRIENDS... OR ANNIE!

165

AND I ALMOST BIT MY YOUNGER SISTER.

I SUCKED BLOOD FROM ONE OF MY BEST FRIENDS.

I HAD A FEELING YOU WOULD BE COMING SOON.

JUST A HUNCH, NOTHING MORE.

YOU ARE LUCKY YOU DID NOT KILL HER.

WELL, THAT IS GOOD.

...BUT DEEP INSIDE ME, THERE'S AN UN-STOPPABLE URGE...

I KNOW I SHOULDN'T DO THESE THINGS...

IT'S NOT GOOD!!

THE ONLY THING THAT CAN STOP YOU NOW...

...IS A STAKE THROUGH THE HEART.

WELL, YOU WERE RIGHT AFTER ALL.

I'VE COME CRAWLING BACK TO YOU.

...BUT I DO FEEL SORRY FOR YOU.

......

YOU MAY NOT BELIEVE ME...

WE HAVE MUCH TO DO BEFORE YOU CAN ASSUME YOUR RIGHTFUL PLACE AS MY ASSISTANT!

BA
(WHOOSH)

COME! WE HAVE WORK TO DO AND NO TIME TO WASTE.

LIKE WHAT?

FIRST OF ALL...

...THAT IS A GOOD QUES- TION.

WELL...

...WE HAVE TO KILL YOU!

GA (GRRK)

CHAPTER 4:
INTO THE NIGHT

AND GOOD-BYE... FOREVER.

FARE-WELL, EVERY-ONE.

TODAY...

...I WILL DIE.

CHAPTER 4:
INTO THE NIGHT

HERE'S DARREN'S FAVORITE: OVEN-ROASTED CHICKEN!

TA·DAAA!

I JUST HAD A FEELING YOU MIGHT WANT TO HAVE THIS!

CALL IT A MOTHER'S INTUITION.

WOW!

WHAT'S THE OCCASION? THIS IS A FEAST!

WELL, WELL! YOU WROTE THAT YOU WANT TO BE LIKE YOUR MOTHER!

YEP!

LOOK, DADDY! I GOT AN A ON MY ESSAY!

WHAT'S THIS? "MY DREAMS FOR THE FUTURE"?

OH, YEAH!

DID YOU SHOW YOUR FATHER YET, ANNIE?

WHAT DO YOU WANT TO BE WHEN YOU GROW UP?

WHAT ABOUT YOU, DARREN?

EWW, NO! YOUR BEARD IS ALL PRICKLY!

HA HA HA!

WHY DIDN'T YOU SAY YOU WANTED TO BE LIKE YOUR FATHER?

COME ON!

OR MAYBE A SOCCER PLAYER.

I BET HE WANTS TO BE A SPIDER-OLOGIST!

I'D WANT TO BE SOMEONE LIKE DAD...

......

...AND RETHINK YOUR OPTIONS NOW, WHILE YOU'VE STILL GOT A CHANCE!

SO HEED MY ADVICE...

LISTEN UP, DARREN. WHEN BOYS GET TO BE YOUR AGE, THEIR MINDS ARE A LOT MORE OPEN TO CHANGE!

...AND MAKE PEN PALS FROM ALL OVER THE PLACE.

I'LL GROW GREAT BIG LEGS SO I CAN WALK AROUND THE WORLD...

OOOOH!

AH! ERR, AHEM!

DADDY'S FACE IS RED!

AHA HA HA HA!

OH DERMOT, STOP BLUSH- ING!

EEK!

GAA (CRAHH)

URGH!

TOKUN (THUMP)

TOKUN

SUU (ZZZ)

SUU

NIGHT, ANNIE ...

PATAN (THUD)

?

TOMOR-ROW...

NIGHT, DAD. NIGHT, MOM.

SEE YOU TOMOR-ROW, SON.

GOOD NIGHT, DARREN.

NEVER MIND! GOOD NIGHT!

THANKS FOR EVERYTHING, MOM AND DAD.

GOODBYE.

MAYBE THAT'S IT.

HA HA HA.

HE'S BEEN ACTING ODDLY FOR SOME TIME NOW, ANGIE.

THERE'S SOMETHING UP WITH HIM.

MAYBE HE'S GOT A GIRL-FRIEND.

GII
(CREAK)

FUWA
(FWOOM)

BA
(WHUD)

I DON'T KNOW.

I THINK...

WHAT'S WRONG WITH HIM, DERMOT!?

LET GO, ANGIE!

DARREN! NO!

...HE MUST HAVE FALLEN.

HE'S NOT... ...BREATHING...

HE'S NOT MOVING!

ZAWA (MURMUR)

ZAWA

HE'S NOT MOVING

HE'S NOT MOVING...

THIS CAN'T BE HAPPENING...

HE'LL BE FINE. HE'S PARALYZED, LIKE STEVE.

HE'LL GET BETTER.

NOW GO INSIDE AND CALL FOR AN AMBULANCE, OKAY?

HE'LL SNAP OUT OF IT.

GABAA
(LURCH)

YOU ARE A BIT GROGGY. THERE IS A LITTLE OF THE POTION STILL LEFT IN YOU.

ARE YOU ALL RIGHT?

S.F.X. GEHO (COUGH) GEHO

THE POISON PUTS YOU INTO A STATE OF NEAR-DEATH, SO IT IS NATURAL THAT YOU ARE NOT QUITE RIGHT FOR A WHILE.

MAYBE THIS WILL HELP...

......

I FEEL DEAD TIRED.

HA HA.

184

GOSO...
(RUSTLE)

YOU DIDN'T LOOK IN HERE, DID YOU?

WHY WOULD I READ A LITTLE BOY'S JOURNAL?

THAT POISON WAS POWERFUL STUFF, STRONG ENOUGH TO STOP A VAMPIRE'S HEART.

ZA
(ZSHH)

IT WILL TAKE A WHILE TO WEAR OFF. GO AHEAD AND WALK SOME OF THE STIFFNESS OUT OF YOUR BONES.

AND HOW DID YOU KNOW THERE WAS A JOURNAL IN HERE?

GYU
(CLENCH)

DAD WAS SCREAMING... AND CRYING...

PIKU
(TWITCH)

I COULD HEAR THEIR VOICES THE ENTIRE TIME.

YOU MADE EVERYONE CRY!

YOU MADE DAD AND MOM AND ANNIE CRY!

AND IT'S ALL YOUR FAULT!

UU (SOB)

I COULD HAVE JUST LEFT AND NEVER COME BACK...

I DIDN'T HAVE TO PLAY DEAD...

NOBODY COMES SEARCHING FOR A DEAD PERSON...

THEY WILL KEEP LOOKING FOR YOU WITHOUT ANY SUCCESS, AN ENDLESS CYCLE OF SORROW WITH NO RELEASE.

THINK OF WHAT HAPPENS IF YOU SIMPLY DISAPPEAR.

HAA (SIGH)

NOW WALK.

I'LL FINISH REPACKING THE SOIL.

186

MADAM OCTA.

THE FLYER.

THE CIRCUS.

... THESE PAST FEW WEEKS.

A LOT HAS HAPPENED ...

IF ONLY I HADN'T...

SO MANY CROSSROADS WHERE MY DESTINY COULD HAVE GONE DIFFERENTLY.

I'M ALREADY ...

DO (WHAM)

HYU (ZIP)

I HAVEN'T SEEN STEVE SINCE THAT ONE DAY, EITHER...

GI (GRRK)

...BUT NO. I CAN'T SEE HIM NOW.

GOSO (RUSTLE)

STEVE!?

::VAMPIRE!?

HOW WAS YOUR WAKE-UP CALL...

...I CAN'T SUMMON ANY STRENGTH!

OH NO! THE POISON'S STILL ACTIVE...

MMPH!

...YOU WERE MY FRIEND...

I THOUGHT...

GUN (WHOOSH)

JIWA (BLSHH)

DO (DMMM)

MEKI
(CRAKK)

GUGUGU
(GRRRGG)

ZEE
(WHEEZE)
ZEE

THIS IS A LEGENDARY MONSTER I'M UP AGAINST, AFTER ALL...

GUCHU
(SCRAPE)

GUCHU

ZEE

ZEE

ZEE

IT'S TOO SOON FOR ME. I NEED TO TRAIN AND PREPARE...

I THOUGHT I'D BE ABLE TO KILL YOU TONIGHT, BUT I WAS WRONG.

NIYAA
(SMIRK)

YOU SHOULD NOT GO TOO FAR.

ZA (ZSHH)

YOU CANNOT AFFORD TO BE SEEN.

IF I DON'T SETTLE MATTERS WITH STEVE NOW, HE'LL COME BACK FOR ME...

WHAT SHOULD I DO? SHOULD I TELL CREPSLEY?

YOU SEEM RATHER PALE TO ME.

ARE YOU SURE YOU ARE ALL RIGHT?

YOU ARE OFFICIALLY DEAD NOW.

IT WOULD NOT DO TO HAVE YOU SPOTTED WALKING AROUND.

I—!

HE'LL COME BACK TO KILL ME!!

MMM

SFX: BAKI (CRACK)

I DON'T CARE. HE'S STILL MY BEST FRIEND...

UH, I MEAN...

I'M FINE. DON'T WORRY...

TERRIBLY
SO...

DOES
IT GET
LONELY?

ALL
ALONE
IN THE
WORLD OF
DARKNESS
...

I'M SO HUNGRY!

I HAVEN'T EATEN SINCE I DIED.

ME TOO!

NOW...

...LET US GO EAT.

SFX: SURI (RUB) SURI

I SQUEEZED HIS HAND, COLD TO THE TOUCH AND SO VERY LARGE.

GYU (SQUEEZE)

SIDE BY SIDE, THE VAMPIRE AND HIS ASSISTANT...

...WE BEGAN WALKING...

...INTO THE NIGHT...

CIRQUE DU FREAK 1 - END

A QUICK GUIDE TO THE STORY OF THE CIRQUE DU FREAK MANGA VERSION (SORT OF)!!

ZAPPAAN (SPLAASH)

I'M TIRED. A SPIDER! I DON'T LIKE THE SUN.

AFTER-WORD SPECIAL

APPARENTLY, SEVERAL CANDIDATES WERE CHOSEN, AND DARREN-SAN, THE AUTHOR, WOULD BE THE FINAL JUDGE. I WAS EXCITED...

I DREW UP A CHAPTER OR TWO WHILE I WORKED AS A MANGA ASSISTANT.

SFX: GARI (SCRATCH) GARI

YOU KNOW A STORY CALLED "CIRQUE DU FREAK"?

A CALL FROM THE EDITOR IN JANUARY OF 2006 BRINGS THE ANSWER.

NO GOOD IDEAS...

ARRRGH!

LATE 2005, A FROG AGONIZES AT HIS DESK.

IF YOU CAN'T PUT TOGETHER A DRAFT, YOU CAN'T DRAW A MANGA!

DESPITE MY YOUNG AND HEARTY AGE, I FALL TERRIBLY SICK AND CAUSE GREAT STRESS TO MY FAMILY.

URRGH!

JUNE 2006: I MOVE INTO A REAL STUDIO IN A HUGE RUSH.

I GET THE CHILLS!

KA (CLICK)

APRIL 2006: MY DRAFT IS ACCEPTED.

SFX: PISHAAA (PZOWWW)

MY BROTHER ALSO DESIGNED SOME CHARACTERS, SUCH AS HANS HANDS, ALEXANDER RIBS AND GERTHA TEETH FOR ME, AS WELL AS SOME OF THE BACKGROUNDS.

THE SCENE WHERE DARREN GRABS THE TICKET.

BY THE WAY, MY OWN BROTHER ALSO TOOK PART IN THE CIRQUE DU FREAK MANGA COMPETITION, AND I USED A PARTICULAR TOUCH OF HIS IN ONE SCENE OF MY FINAL VERSION. (HIS IDEA WAS BETTER THAN MINE...)

I HOPE TO DO JUSTICE TO THIS EPIC TALE, AND FOR THAT I'LL NEED ALL YOUR SUPPORT!

I'LL DO MY BEST NOT TO EMBARRASS MYSELF IN FRONT OF EVERYONE!

...NOT TO MENTION DARREN SHAN FOR HIS INCREDIBLE STORY, THE PRINTERS, AND OF COURSE, ALL THE FANS WHO ENJOYED IT.

PEKO (BOW)

I AM GRATEFUL TO EVERYONE INVOLVED IN MAKING THIS BOOK: MY BROTHER, STAFF, EDITOR, LOVING FAMILY AND FRIENDS...

CIRQUE DU FREAK ①

DARREN SHAN
TAKAHIRO ARAI

Translation: Stephen Paul　　•　　Lettering: AndWorld Design
Original Cover Design: Hitoshi SHIRAYAMA + Bay Bridge Studio

DARREN SHAN Vol. 1 © 2006 by Darren Shan, Takahiro ARAI. All
rights reserved. Original Japanese edition published in Japan in 2006
by Shogakukan Inc., Tokyo. Artworks reproduction rights in U.S.A. and
Canada arranged with Shogakukan Inc. through Tuttle-Mori Agency,
Inc., Tokyo.

Yen Press
Hachette Book Group
237 Park Avenue, New York, NY 10017

Visit our Web sites at www.HachetteBookGroup.com and
www.YenPress.com.

Yen Press is an imprint of Hachette Book Group, Inc. The Yen Press
name and logo are trademarks of Hachette Book Group, Inc.

First Yen Press Edition: June 2009

ISBN: 978-0-7595-3041-6

10　9　8　7　6　5　4　3　2　1

BVG

Printed in the United States of America

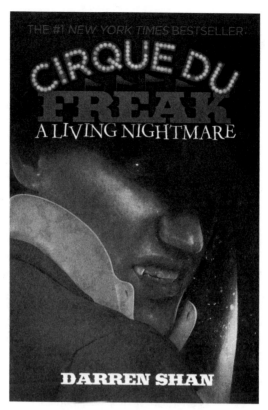

CHECK OUT
AN EXCERPT OF
THE BOOK
CIRQUE DU FREAK

Please flip your book over to enjoy a couple chapters of the
prose version of *Cirque Du Freak*, currently in stores!

but the bell rang just as I was hitting my stride, so we lost nine–seven.

As we were leaving the field, Alan Morris ran toward us, panting and red-faced. They're my three best friends: Steve Leopard, Tommy Jones, and Alan Morris. We must be the weirdest four people in the whole world, because only one of us — Steve — has a nickname.

"Look what I found!" Alan yelled, waving a soggy piece of paper around under our noses.

"What is it?" Tommy asked, trying to grab it.

"It's —," Alan began, but stopped when Mr. Dalton shouted at us.

"You four! Inside!" he roared.

"We're coming, Mr. Dalton!" Steve roared back. Steve is Mr. Dalton's favorite and gets away with stuff that the rest of us couldn't do. Like when he uses swearwords sometimes in his stories. If I put in some of the words Steve has, I'd have been kicked out long ago.

But Mr. Dalton has a soft spot for Steve, because he's special. Sometimes he's brilliant in class and gets everything right, while other times he can't even spell his own name. Mr. Dalton says he's somewhat of an *idiot savant,* which mean he's a stupid genius!

Anyway, even though he's Mr. Dalton's pet, not even Steve can get away with showing up late for class. So whatever Alan had, it would have to wait. We trudged back to class, sweaty and tired after the game, and began our next lesson.

Little did I know that Alan's mysterious piece of paper was to change my life forever. For the worse!

"I thought I'd stay in here and admire the view," I said, leaning back on the toilet seat.

"Quit joking," he said. "We were down five–one when I came in. We're probably six or seven down now. We need you." He was talking about soccer. We play a game every lunchtime. My team normally wins but we'd lost a lot of our best players. Dave Morgan broke his leg. Sam White transferred to another school when his family moved. And Danny Curtain had stopped playing soccer in order to spend lunch hanging out with Sheila Leigh, the girl he likes. Idiot!

I'm our best forward. There are better defenders and midfielders, and Tommy Jones is the best goalkeeper in the whole school. But I'm the only one who can stand up front and score four or five times a day without fail.

"Okay," I said, standing. "I'll save you. I've scored a hat trick every day this week. It would be a pity to stop now."

We passed the older guys — smoking around the sinks as usual — and hurried to my locker so I could change into my cleats. I used to have a great pair, which I won in a writing competition. But the laces snapped a few months ago and the rubber along the sides started to fall off. And then my feet grew! The pair I have now are okay, but they're not the same.

We were down eight–three when I got on the field. It wasn't a real field, just a long stretch of grass with painted goalposts at either end. Whoever painted them was a total idiot. He put the crossbar too high at one end and too low at the other!

"Never fear, Hotshot Shan is here!" I shouted as I ran onto the field. A lot of players laughed or groaned, but I could see my teammates picking up and our opponents growing worried.

I made a great start and scored two goals inside a minute. It looked like we might come back to draw or win. But time ran out. If I'd arrived earlier we'd have been okay, when we first met. My mom says I was drawn to his wildness, but I just thought he was a great guy to be with. He had a fierce temper and threw scary tantrums when he lost it, but I simply ran away when that happened and came back again once he'd calmed down.

Steve's reputation had softened over the years — his mom took him to see a lot of good counselors who taught him how to control himself — but he was still a minor legend in the schoolyard and not someone you messed with, even if you were bigger and older than him.

"Hey, Steve," I called back. "I'm in here." I hit the door so he'd know which one I was behind.

He hurried over and I opened the door. He smiled when he saw me sitting down with my pants on. "Did you puke?" he asked.

"No," I said.

"Do you think you're gonna?"

"Maybe," I said. Then I leaned forward all of a sudden and made a sick noise. Bluurgh! But Steve Leopard knew me too well to be fooled.

"Give my boots a polish while you're down there," he said, and laughed when I pretended to spit on his shoes and rub them with a sheet of toilet paper.

"Did I miss anything in class?" I asked, sitting up.

"Nah," he said. "The usual crap."

"Did you do your history homework?" I asked.

"It doesn't have to be done until tomorrow, does it?" he asked, getting worried. Steve's always forgetting about homework.

"The day after tomorrow," I told him.

"Oh," he said, relaxing. "Even better. I thought . . ." He stopped and frowned. "Hold on," he said. "Today's Thursday. The day after tomorrow would be . . ."

"Got you!" I yelled, punching him on the shoulder.

"Ow!" he shouted. "That hurt." He rubbed his arm but I could tell he wasn't really hurt. "Are you coming out?" he asked then.

CHAPTER ONE

I WAS IN THE BATHROOM at school, sitting down on the toilet, humming a song. I had my pants on. I'd come in near the end of English class, feeling sick. My teacher, Mr. Dalton, is great about things like that. He's smart and knows when you're faking and when you're being serious. He took one look at me when I raised my hand and said I was ill, then nodded his head and told me to go to the bathroom.

"Throw up whatever's making you sick, Darren," he said, "then get your behind back in here."

I wish every teacher was as understanding as Mr. Dalton.

In the end, I didn't get sick, but still felt queasy, so I stayed on the toilet. I heard the bell ring for the end of class and everybody came rushing out on their lunch break. I wanted to join them but knew Mr. Dalton would be angry if he saw me in the yard so soon. He doesn't get mad if you trick him but he goes quiet and won't speak to you for a while, and that's almost worse than being shouted at.

So, there I was, humming, watching my watch, waiting. Then I heard someone calling my name.

"Darren! Hey, Darren! Have you fallen in or what?"

I grinned. It was Steve Leopard, my best friend. Steve's real last name was Leonard, but everyone called him Steve Leopard. And not just because the names sound alike. Steve used to be what my mom calls "a wild child." He raised hell wherever he went, got into fights, stole from stores. One day — he was still in a stroller — he found a sharp stick and prodded passing women with it (no prizes for guessing where he stuck it!).

He was feared and despised everywhere he went. But not by me. I've been his best friend since kindergarten, friends, or teachers. Nobody's. I'm not even going to tell you the name of my town or country. I don't dare.

Anyway, that's enough of an introduction. If you're ready, let's begin. If this were a made-up story, it would begin at night, with a storm blowing and owls hooting and rattling noises under the bed. But this is a real story, so I have to begin where it really started.

It started in a toilet.

INTRODUCTION

My parents practically hollered the roof down when they found out what I'd done — the tarantula had cost quite a lot of money. They said I was irresponsible, and from that day on they never again let me have a pet, not even an ordinary garden spider.

I started with that tale from the past for two reasons. One will become obvious as this book unfolds. The other reason is:

This is a true story.

I don't expect you to believe me — I wouldn't believe it myself if I hadn't lived it — but it is. Everything I describe in this book happened, just as I tell it.

The thing about real life is, when you do something stupid, it normally costs you. In books, the heroes can make as many mistakes as they like. It doesn't matter what they do, because everything works out in the end. They'll beat the bad guys and put things right and everything ends up cool.

In real life, vacuum cleaners kill spiders. If you cross a busy road without looking, you get whacked by a car. If you fall out of a tree, you break some bones.

Real life's nasty. It's cruel. It doesn't care about heroes and happy endings and the way things should be. In real life, bad things happen. People die. Fights are lost. Evil often wins.

I just wanted to make that clear before I began.

One more thing: my name isn't really Darren Shan. Everything's true in this book, *except* for names. I've had to change them because . . . well, by the time you get to the end, you'll understand.

I haven't used *any* real names, not mine, my sister's, my

INTRODUCTION

I'VE ALWAYS BEEN FASCINATED BY spiders. I used to collect them when I was younger. I'd spend hours rooting through the dusty old shed at the bottom of our garden, hunting the cobwebs for lurking eight-legged predators. When I found one, I'd bring it in and let it loose in my bedroom.

It used to drive my mom crazy!

Usually, the spider would slip away after no more than a day or two, never to be seen again, but sometimes they hung around longer. I had one who made a cobweb above my bed and stood guard for almost a month. Going to sleep, I used to imagine the spider creeping down, crawling into my mouth, sliding down my throat, and laying loads of eggs in my belly. The baby spiders would hatch after a while and eat me alive, from the inside out.

I loved being scared when I was little.

When I was nine, my mom and dad gave me a small tarantula. It wasn't poisonous or very big, but it was the greatest gift I'd ever received. I played with that spider almost every waking hour of the day. Gave it all sorts of treats: flies and cockroaches and tiny worms. Spoiled it rotten.

Then, one day, I did something stupid. I'd been watching a cartoon in which one of the characters was sucked up by a vacuum cleaner. No harm came to him. He squeezed out of the bag, dusty and dirty and mad as hell. It was very funny.

So funny, I tried it myself. With the tarantula.

Needless to say, things didn't happen quite like they did in the cartoon. The spider was ripped to pieces. I cried a lot, but it was too late for tears. My pet was dead, it was my fault, and there was nothing I could do about it.